Disclaimer

Hand on hearts to you we swear
as far as we are both aware
the contents of this book are true...
we hope it all works out for you.

Odd harmless fibs, alleged lies,
are just a literary device.
So please, we beg you, don't resort
to pursuing us in court.

We have a watertight defence:
it's called poetic license.

First Published 2019
Tiny Tree Children's Books (an imprint of Matthew James Publishing Ltd)
Unit 46, Goyt Mill, Marple, Stockport, SK6 7HX

www.tinytreebooks.com

ISBN: 978-1-910265-74-1

Celebrity Endorsements

"Reminds me of my own work."
PROFESSOR VERITY INCREDIBLE

"This book changed my life."
ROB O. TANDROID

"Explains a lot."
WARREN E. WOLFE

"Makes me wish I weren't a carnivore."
DR. S. HARK

"Really upped my basketball game."
QUETZALCOATL

"I give this book, cauliflower, and asparagus
to all my favourite colleagues."
ALLY GATOR

TO MUM AND DAD, FOR SETTING ME ON THE POETICAL PATH.
ALSO TO MARK, AND MY ORIGINAL BLUEBERRY VAMPIRE.
JONAH WILLIAM: EAT MORE VEGETABLES!

S.K.

FOR MY PARENTS, JIANNA AND AARON;
AND FOR CHRIS.
ALSO A SPECIAL THANKS TO OWEN.

J.J.H.

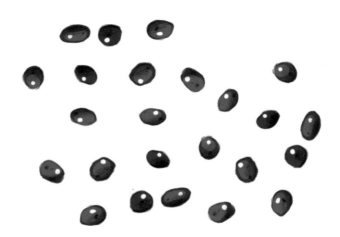

About this Book

VEGETABLE POWERS HAVE REMAINED
TOO LONG OBSCURE AND UNEXPLAINED.
FRUITS ALSO LEND YOU SECRET SKILLS
ON TOP OF NORMAL FRUITY THRILLS.

DO YOU WANT TO LEARN TO FLY
OR TRAIN TO BE A PRIVATE-EYE?
EMANCIPATE YOUR INNER TIGER?
OR SHOW UP ON A COUNTER (GEIGER'S)?

FOR POWERS BEYOND YOUR WILDEST DREAMS,
FORGET ABOUT SORCERY, STEROIDS, OR CREAMS...
JUST CRUNCH YOUR VEGETABLE OR FRUIT:
HEY PRESTO! YOU'LL BE CUDDLY CUTE,
A DANCE SENSATION, SUPER-BRAVE...
WHATEVER SCRUMMY SKILL YOU CRAVE.

DON'T WASTE A MOMENT, DON'T DELAY
GET MUNCHING YOUR FIRST FIVE TODAY.

Table of Contents

Part 1 Enhanced Humans

Part 2 Inner Animals

Part 3 Supernatural Food-nomena

Half Your Plate

Science boffins advocate
the proper way to fill a plate
requires half be veg or fruit...
the other half – who gives a hoot?
Yes – rules and regulations say
for fruit and veg... have 5-per-day
five-a-day or half your plate
and try not to regurgitate.

Part 1
Enhanced Humans

Apple Basketballer

HERE'S A SECRET THE AZTECS KNEW
WHEN THEY PLAYED BALL IN 1402:

EACH APPLE YOU CHOMP, CORE AND ALL
BUILDS YOUR BOUNCE FOR BASKETBALL.

PRE-GAME, SCOFF AN APPLE DISH —
THEN DRIBBLE, DRIBBLE, SHOOT...

SWISH!

THE ANCIENT MAYA OF CHICHEN ITZA
EVEN PUT APPLES ON THEIR PIZZA.

WHILE THE INCAS AT MACHU PICCHU
OFTEN ENJOYED AN APPLE STEW.

Spinach Sprinter

SPINACH UNFINISHED
        WILL GREATLY DIMINISH

YOUR STRENGTH
        AND TURN YOU THINNISH.

IT'S IRON YOU NEED,
        TO SUCCEED, AT FULL SPEED;

AND THAT IS WHY
        SPRINTERS CHOOSE SPINACH.

Rhubarb Rapunzel

To grow your hair out very long,

and make it extra thick and strong,

obtain a rhubarb pie or crumble,

and swallow it without a grumble.

Cucumber Cutie-Pie

REGRETTING SOME PRIOR BEHAVIOUR MOST HORRIBLE?
DO PEOPLE NOW THINK YOU ARE LESS THAN ADORABLE?

REMEMBER THE CUCUMBER CUTIE-PIE'S HABIT
OF MUNCHING ON CUCUMBER – JUST LIKE A RABBIT.

SOON YOU'LL BE CUTE AS A BUTTON – OR BUNNY,
THEY'LL BE PINCHING YOUR CHEEKS, CALLING YOU 'HONEY'!

AS STRATEGIES GO...
                    IT'S UNORTHODOX
BUT BLESS YOUR CUCUMBERY CUTE COTTON SOCKS!

YOUR OLD MISDEMEANOURS FORGOT AND FORGIVEN,
AT LEAST 'TIL THE CUCUMBER'S OUT OF YOUR SYSTEM.

Paw-Paw Virtues

PAPAYA – ALSO CALLED PAW-PAW
TASTES FABULOUS, BUT WHAT'S IT FOR?
YOU CAN USE IT TO DE-WORM
OR FRIGHTEN AN OBNOXIOUS GERM.

IT ALSO CONFERS SAINTLY QUALITIES,
LIKE KINDLINESS, AND GENEROSITY.

THEY SAY PATIENCE IS A VIRTUE...

I GUESS IT PROBABLY CAN'T HURT YOU.

eat more Carica papaya.

11

Dandelion Dancer

CONGA, TAP, HAKA, JIVE,
HULA, ROBOT, WALTZ, GLIDE,
OH TO HAVE COORDINATION!
FANCY FOOTWORK! HEAD ROTATION!

HOW TO GET THE NIMBLE CHARMS
OF WOBBLE-HIPS AND JELLY-ARMS?

WALLFLOWER STANDING ALL FORLORN,
TANGO TO YOUR NEAREST LAWN.
A HUMBLE YELLOW-FLOWERED WEED
HOLDS THE GIFT YOU SORELY NEED.

YES! IT SEEMS INCREDIBLE,
BUT DANDELIONS ARE EDIBLE:
FOR EPIC DANCING STYLE AND GRACE
SIMPLY STUFF THEM IN YOUR FACE.

CHA-CHA-CHÁ!

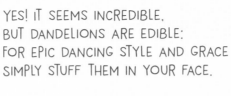

13

Cauliflower Kindness

THERE'S ALWAYS ONE IN EVERY GROUP:
A CRANKY, GRUMPY NINCOMPOOP...

OBNOXIOUS SNAPPY CROCODILE,
QUICK TO ANGER, SLOW TO SMILE.

PUT THEM IN A KINDER MOOD
WITH A SPECIAL KIND OF FOOD:

BETTER THAN A BUNCH OF FLOWERS
IS A LUNCH OF CAULIFLOWERS!

Celery Sleuth

Every excellent detective
needs a snack to be effective.
With lovely perfume, juice, and crunch,
sleuths choose celery to munch.
    Even if stringy, it can be used
    for pointing at criminals: *J'accuse!*

Part 2
Inner Animals

Pomegranate Pronghorn

Pomegranate Pronghorn enjoys the great outdoors,
prancing proudly on all fours.

Shiny jewels of juicy seeds
help her run at super speeds.

P.P. is especially quick
on a well-sprung pogo-stick.

Shallot Sea Otter

Sea otters float,
relaxed on their backs,
obsessed with possessing
new shalloty snacks.

Exquisite shallots,
clutched twixt dainty claws,
are nibbled with relish
and licking of paws.

20

RELAX ON THE SHORE
    WITH A SHALLOT OR TWO
TO FEED THE SEA OTTER
    INSIDE OF YOU.

EAT A WHOLE LOT OF THEM:
    IT WILL EMERGE
(YOUR INNER SEA OTTER),
    SOON TO SUBMERGE

IN THE GREEN SWELLS
    OF A WARM KELPY SEA...
UTTERLY, OTTERLY, SWIMMINGLY FREE.

21

tomato tiger

All types of tomato T.T. loves to devour
cherry, plum, beefsteak, tinned, sweet, and sour.
A dripping tomato impaled on each claw
scrumptious with ketchup, or just eaten raw.

Tomato, tomato, burning bright
in the greenhouse of the night
what dread vegetable* inventor
designed that red, delicious centre?
What dread hands? What dread heart?
Could forge such skin and pericarp?
Here endeth the tomato anatomy lesson.
Sorry for this weird digression.

*ARE TOMATOES VEGETABLES OR FRUITS? TOMATO TIGERS DON'T GIVE TWO HOOTS.

To camouflage
with your surrounds

Eat lots of carrots –
heaps and mounds.

In no time
you'll be changing hue –

Vermillion, emerald,
amethyst, blue...

Get the chameleon's cool mystique,
and always win at hide-and-seek.

24

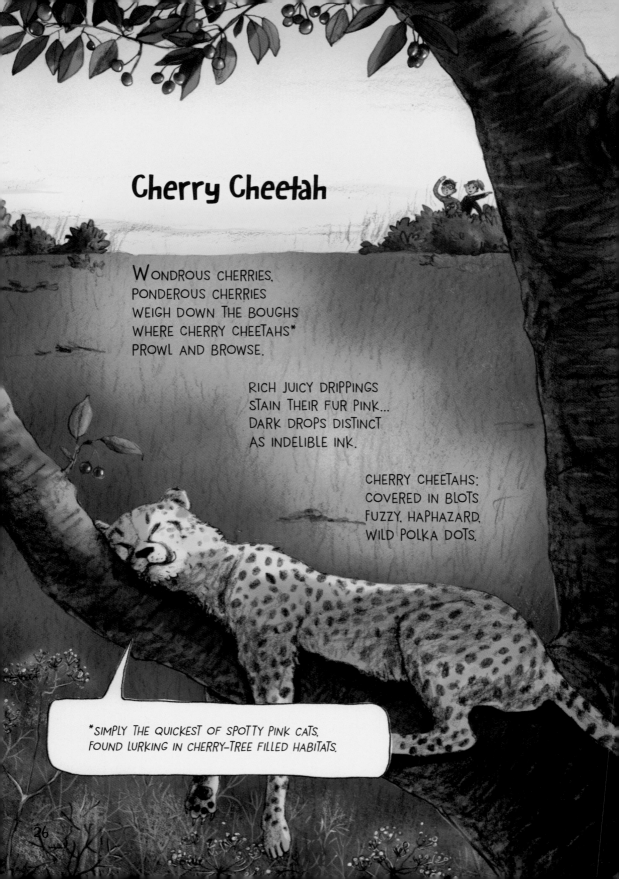

Cherry Cheetah

WONDROUS CHERRIES,
PONDEROUS CHERRIES
WEIGH DOWN THE BOUGHS
WHERE CHERRY CHEETAHS*
PROWL AND BROWSE.

RICH JUICY DRIPPINGS
STAIN THEIR FUR PINK...
DARK DROPS DISTINCT
AS INDELIBLE INK.

CHERRY CHEETAHS:
COVERED IN BLOTS
FUZZY, HAPHAZARD,
WILD POLKA DOTS.

*SIMPLY THE QUICKEST OF SPOTTY PINK CATS,
FOUND LURKING IN CHERRY-TREE FILLED HABITATS.

Fennel Flamingo

To strut your stuff like a hip flamingo
Eat some fennel – that's it – bingo!

Fennel leaves are wispy light
You'll sprout up to an elegant height
With delicate stilts for wading in ponds
Soft pink neck and feathery fronds.

Be as beautiful as the sunrise
Over Amboseli skies.

Mushroom Monkey

To grow a tail that's prehensile*
you needn't resort to anything vile
simply sup on a mushroom dish,
of whichever type you wish.

PORTOBELLO, OYSTER, SHIITAKE, OR BUTTON
NO MATTER THE FUNGUS: BE A GLUTTON!
    ... JUST MAKE SURE IT ISN'T MAGIC,
    TO AVOID AN END THAT'S TRAGIC...

MUSHROOMS HELP YOU LEAP ABOUT,
SWING FROM RAFTERS, HOOT AND SHOUT
    OO-OO-AH-AH, SQUEAK AND WAIL
    WHILE SWINGING BY YOUR FANCY TAIL.

*SO MUCH MORE THAN A TAIL THAT WAGS,
IT'S A TAIL THAT HOLDS AND GRABS!

Part 3
Supernatural Food—nomena

Prairie Fig Fairy

IF YOU'D PREFER TO BE A FAIRY
FIND A FIG TREE ON A PRAIRIE*
SOMEWHERE NEAR SOME FOSSIL DIGS
CLIMB UP AND STUFF YOURSELF WITH FIGS!

CURIOUS POWERS CAN BE FOUND
IN FIG TREES ROOTED IN FOSSIL GROUND.

YOUR HEAD MIGHT SPIN, ALL AIRY AND LIGHT —
ON GOSSAMER WINGS, YOU COULD EVEN TAKE FLIGHT.

FIG FAIRIES HAVE SPARKLE AND PIZZAZZ GALORE...
THEY CAN TRANSFORM A NEWT TO AN ICHTHYOSAUR.

IF IT WASN'T FOR FIG TREES
ON WIDE-OPEN PRAIRIES,
FABULOUS FLUTTERING FAIRIES MIGHT
BE JUST AS EXTINCT AS THE AMMONITE.

*AS YOU KNOW, PRAIRIES ARE WIDE GRASSY LANDS
WITH DINOSAUR BONES JUST UNDER THE SANDS

Blackberry Beast

Autumn in the countryside –
    cloudless skies, blue and wide:

Perfect time to comb the brambles
    while you're out on rural rambles.

Gorge on berries, plump and sweet,
    but stay light upon your feet.
Strange events sometimes transpire
    near a patch of prickly briar...

        By the thorns inside your thumbs,
        something wild and woolly comes!

What beast is this with purple cheeks?
    It's giving everyone the creeps!
Its paws are icky sticky blue...
    You'll stain if it touches you.

        Run, run, run! Run-run-run-leap!
        Watch out for that herd of sheep!

Your clothes are torn to little shreds,
    your face is stained in mauves and reds!
    Your woolly threads have gotten snagged!
    Your hair looks like you have been dragged
    backwards through the shrubbery...
        Oh what is this skulduggery?

And how is it that your friends never
    see you and the creature both together?

Kale Kraken

Kraken eats kale everywhere
    on the ground and in the air...

But his favourite place to grub
    is deep within the bathing tub.

Grape Griffin

Do you want to join the pride?
or grow a lion's majestic backside?

First things firstly, please locate
        half a dozen wine-dark grapes.
Guzzle skin and flesh, and juice...
        shifting shape's not just for Zeus!

Your arms and hands will turn to talons
        (do try not to lose your balance).

Your shoulders will sprout feathery wings,
and through a beak you'll witter things –

Like: "Golly gosh, i've got back paws!
        And lots of rather pointy claws!
        And... *six* limbs instead of four
        like a flea, or a dragon, or a centaur!"

Your rump will be lion; your front eagle,
all supernatural, freaky and regal.

                Bit weird in a comparative anatomy sense,
                but no weirder than angels – in your defence.

Okra Photographer

Bashful water creatures won't cooperate for photos Little mermaids are all wriggly, not to mention ogopogos.*

You might catch half a flipper, but it's almost always blurry... What is that? It could be scaly, barnacled, or furry!

For water-wildlife photoshoots, aquatic or marine, Fit for publication in a decent magazine.

YOU NEED A LITTLE SOMETHING MORE THAN CAMERA TECHNIQUE...
SCRUMPTIOUS SLIMY OKRA IS THE ANSWER THAT YOU SEEK!

OKRA LOVERS ARE APPEALING TO ALL SORTS OF WATER CREATURES...
THEY WON'T MIND POSING PEACEFULLY FOR PHOTOGRAPHIC FEATURES.

SNAP OBLIGING OGOPOGOS IN LAKE OKANAGAN,
OR MERRY LITTLE MERMAIDS IN THE HEART OF COPENHAGEN.

JUST AS LONG AS YOU HAVE OKRA DIGESTING IN YOUR TUMMY
THE WATER MONSTERS WILL REMAIN AGREEABLE AND CHUMMY.

*THE LOCH NESS MONSTER'S CANADIAN RELATIONS
A LITTLE BIT LESS FAMOUS, WITH GREENER COLOURATIONS.

41

turnip telekinetic

TO MOVE SOME OBJECTS WITH YOUR MIND

SEVERAL TURNIPS YOU MUST FIND.

ROAST ON HIGH FOR HALF AN HOUR,

MASH WITH BUTTER, AND DEVOUR.

SOON YOU'LL ACHIEVE TELEKINESIS

(AT LEAST THAT IS OUR HUMBLE THESIS).

Guacamole Gargoyle

Guacamole gargoyle loves smashed avocado,

laced with chilli — for bravado;

a dash of salt, a squeeze of lime —

looks pretty ugly... but tastes divine.

43

Part 4
21st Century Essentials

Honeydew Hacker

TO HACK THE GOVERNMENT'S COMPUTERS
YOU NEED INCENTIVE, GUILE, AND ROUTERS.
ALL THESE SKILLS YOU MAY ACCRUE
THROUGH MUNCHING ON A HONEYDEW...
YOU MIGHT GET REALLY STICKY CHEEKS
BUT YOU'LL MAKE FRIENDS IN WIKILEAKS.
JUST BEWARE THE SECRET SERVICE!
SOMETIMES MELONS MAKE THEM NERVOUS.

Onion... Oh the Humanity!

A STRANGE SIDE-EFFECT OF ONION CONSUMING:
YOU WILL BECOME MORE HUMAN THAN HUMAN.

TO TACKLE THE TURING TEST* FIRST TIME ROUND,
ANDROIDS EAT ONIONS FRESH FROM THE GROUND.

ANDROIDS MIGHT DREAM OF ELECTRIC SHEEP,
BUT REAL ONIONS MAKE THEM WEEP.

*ALAN TURING DEVISED A TEST TO REVEAL
THE HEART OF THE ROBOT: MACHINES THAT FEEL.

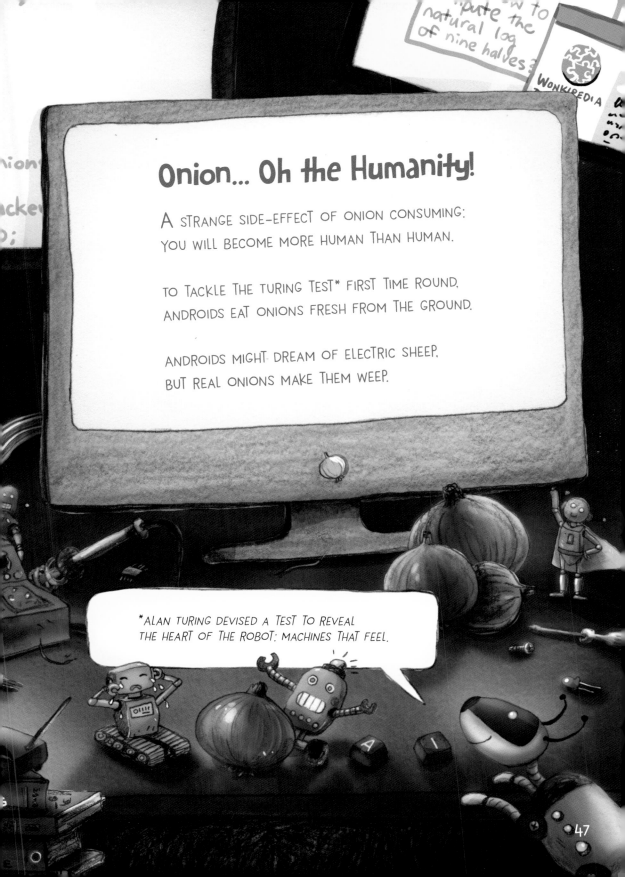

Eggplant Empathizer

To truly master the art of compassion,
    eggplant dishes you mustn't ration.

        In France they call it aubergine
        which is French for "so not-mean"*

Eat your eggplant slice by slice
    and feel yourself becoming nice.

Soon you'll be kind, loving and caring:
    you'll even begin to feel like sharing
        your aubergine and other things,
            like chocolates and onion rings.

Banana Boomeranging

THE STICKS YOU THROW NEVER COME BACK?
COULD BE POTASSIUM YOU LACK.

EAT BANANAS FOR NO END
OF THROWING STICKS AROUND A BEND.

BANANA BENEFITS DON'T STOP THERE...
THEY EXTEND TO UNDERWEAR:
FROM THE FIBROUS LEAFY PLANTS
HIPSTERS FASHION UNDERPANTS.

Lemon Anti-Depression

DOES LIFE FEEL LIKE A DULL GREY ACHE?
EVEN AFTER A WHOLE CREAM CAKE?

IF YOU'RE OUT OF PEP AND ZING,
LEMONS CAN SOLVE EVERYTHING.

LICK THE JUICE – SQUINT-SCRUNCH-WINCE!
FEEL THE RUSH OF ENDORPHINS!

LEMON MERINGUE PIE, DRIZZLE AND SORBET
WASH THE STINGS AND ACHES AWAY...

ZESTY SCENTS INFUSE YOUR BRAIN
BOUNCING AWAY ANY SIGNALS OF PAIN.

FEEL THE GREY CLOUDS LIFT WITH LEMON...
SLICES OF RAPTURE, CITRUS HEAVEN.

Orange Origami Whiz

SURE YOU CAN FOLD A PAPER FAN
OR EVEN A PLANE – ANYONE CAN!

BUT IF YOU'RE FINDING IT A CHORE
TO ORIGAMI SOMETHING MORE,

DON'T MAKE ANY SACRIFICES!
EAT A BUNCH MORE ORANGE SLICES.

NEXT, FOLD PAPER INTO THINGS
WITH RUNNING LEGS AND FLAPPING WINGS.

JUST DON'T FOLD IT LIKE A KLUTZ...
SPARE YOURSELF THE PAPER CUTS.

Cabbage Charisma

If you lack in magnetism
don't give in to pessimism!
On cabbage dishes you must gnaw —
stewed, fermented, or coleslaw.

Don't worry if you start to bloat;
charisma is the antidote.
Sure, your cheeks may squeak a bit
but your character's a hit!

It's well known the charismatic
can be somewhat aromatic.

Passionfruit People Power

IS POWER ABOUT...
        COMMAND AND AUTHORITY?
OR IS IT THE ABSENCE
        OF INFERIORITY?

EVERY PASSIONFRUIT
        GRACING THE VINE
GROWS FROM A FLOWER
        EQUALLY FINE.

TRUE POWER IS
        TO UNDERSTAND
PEOPLE ARE PRECIOUS.
        THEN TO DEMAND
EQUAL RIGHTS
        ACROSS THE BOARD!

PASSION IS MIGHTIER
        THAN THE SWORD.

True Grit* Beans

WITH ANY LUCK YOU'LL LIVE A LIFE
      FREE OF CARES AND DREADFUL STRIFE,
MAY NO CATASTROPHE OR TROUBLE
      EVER BURST YOUR HAPPY BUBBLE.

BUT JUST IN CASE DISASTER HITS,
      PLEASE DON'T GO AND FALL TO BITS,
OR CHOOSE DESPAIR OR CALL IT QUITS!
      USE SOME OF YOUR TRUEST GRITS.

PERSEVERANCE, STRENGTH, RESOLVE –
      ALL THESE THINGS YOU CAN EVOLVE
BY REGULARLY CHOOSING BEANS:
      BLACK ONES, KIDNEY ONES, AND GREENS.

*TRUE GRIT IS SOMETHING FOUND WITHIN
THAT HELPS YOU TAKE THINGS ON THE CHIN.

Part 5
Otherworldly Powers

Asparagus
Alien-Spotting

Travellers from outer space
planet hop without a trace...

They land on earth, refuel, relax,
fix the warp drive, buy knickknacks,
all the while in full disguise,
hidden from beady human eyes.

But eat some fresh asparagus spears
and all the cloaking disappears!
Overnight get second sight
for alien spotting, left and right!

When you see them, just be brave:
practice a friendly alien wave.

Some aliens will find it curious...
others will be super furious.

Blueberry Vampire

Is count dracula your hero?
That's okay, you're not a weirdo.
Want fangs for biting adversaries?
Gorge yourself on blueberries.

Suck the juices, watch them spatter,
Gush and drip a purple matter.
Delicious sweet intoxicants
Full of antioxidants.

Soon you'll get vampire skills -
Like looking good in shirts with frills
And high-collared swishy capes -
Just please beware of wooden stakes.

PRACTICE YOUR NEW VAMPY POWERS
BY FLYING OFF THE TOP OF TOWERS
(DO THIS AS A BAT OF COURSE;
TO COMBAT GRAVITATIONAL FORCE).

VAMPIRE BATS CAN BE CUTE
ESPECIALLY WHEN EATING FRUIT.

Watermelon Werewolf

FOR GROWING HAIRS UPON YOUR CHEST
WATERMELON IS THE BEST.

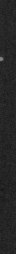

SLAVER AND CRUNCH, CHEW AND SWALLOW
TILL THE RIND IS FULLY HOLLOW.

CRUNCH THE PIPS, OR SPIT THEM OUT,
HOWL AND HOWL AND LOPE ABOUT

(WITH TABLE MANNERS THUS SUPPRESSED,
YOUR FRETFUL CHUMS MAY BE DISTRESSED).

RIP IT APART; DON'T USE A SPOON,
WOLF IT DOWN BY THE LIGHT OF THE MOON.

Longevity Sphinx

Riddle me this – on the double!
        A type of weed but it's no trouble.
Lives in the ocean, but doesn't swim.
        Can be mulched, on a whim.
What in the world could it be?
        Appears to have leaves, but is no tree.
Fed up with the mystery?
        It's seaweed – algae from the sea!

Seeking to live to a ripe old age?
        Seaweed meals are all the rage.
Plus, seaweed's rich in iodine
        (You'll soon develop the body of a lion).
You'll still be human above the neck...
        Gobble some sushi – what the heck!

Sphinxes live till they're really ancient
But to see if it works – you'll have to be patient.

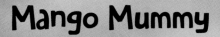

Mango Mummy

Peel the skin and suck the stone

mango flesh off mango bone.

viscous juices, sweet and tart

re-animate the mortal spark.

after wrapping and embalming,

mango can be very calming.

Zucchini Zombie Antidote

ZOMBIES ARE SCARY,
      EVERYONE KNOWS –
IF YOU GET BITTEN –
      SOON IT SHOWS.
BUT THERE IS A NEAT VACCINE –
      YUMMY AND SQUISHY AND LOVELY GREEN.
IF YOU EAT ENOUGH ZUCCHINI
      ZOMBIES CAN'T TURN YOU INTO A MEANIE.

Part 6

Weird & Wonderful

Pumpkin Spelunking

Had it with scaredy-cat, cave-fearing bumpkins?
Chill with spelunkers and dine upon pumpkins!

The best cave explorers munch pumpkin routinely
And enter each cavern serenely, quite keenly.

Pitch blackness and damp claustrophobic conditions,
Stalactites, stalagmites, sad Greek musicians.

FLUTTERING MOTHS AND FLITTERING BATS,
WANDERING MINERS WITH LAMPS ON THEIR HATS.

ASTHMATIC CANARIES, LONG VERTICAL DROPS,
TUNNEL COLLAPSES AND HOSTILE CYCLOPS,

GHOSTS OUT OF HADES IN UNDERGROUND LAIRS,
NEWLY AWAKENED CROSS GRIZZLY BEARS...

ALL OF THESE HURDLES YOU CAN SURMOUNT
WHEN YOU EAT PUMPKIN BEFORE SETTING OUT.

WHEN STUFF GETS SCARY, DEEP IN THE CAVERNS,
BANISH THE DARKNESS WITH JACK-O'-LANTERNS!

Pea Soup Invisibility

WITHOUT A DOUBT, INVISIBILITY
IS A CRACKING CAPABILITY.

TO HIDE YOURSELF FROM PRYING GLANCES
JUST GIVE PEAS A LOT OF CHANCES.

SPECIFICALLY, EAT PEA SOUP:
NOT TOO RUNNY, NOT TOO... GLOOP.

Radish Radioactivity

GETTING BITTEN BY A RADIOACTIVE BUG

OR TAKING A PRESCRIPTION DRUG

ARE TWO WAYS TO GET RADIOACTIVE-ISH.

THE THIRD WAY IS TO EAT A RADISH.

Squash Sasquatch

TO GROW LARGE OF BODY AND FEET,
COOK A SQUASH AND EAT, EAT, EAT!

BIGFEET, SASQUATCHES OR YETI
LOVE A BIT OF SQUASH SPAGHETTI.

THEY RELEASE THEIR INNER STRESS
CAMPING IN THE WILDERNESS.

RAMPAGE THROUGH THE EVERGREENS
LIKE A BIGFOOT BY ALL MEANS...

OR LOUNGE BESIDE THE FIRE-PIT
WITH BUTTERNUT ROASTING ON A SPIT.

PRACTICE ROARING LIKE CHEWBACCA
TO PUT OFF ANY WILD ATTACKER.

COUGARS, BEARS AND MOSQUITOES
WON'T GO NEAR YOUR BIGFOOT TOES.

Peach Pear **Plum** Pineapple
Precognition

Knowing the future's your best shot
for winning a mega-bazillion-jackpot.

Want to predict events to come?
Eat a peach, a pear, and plum,
together in a wholesome blend
with pineapple and your best friend.

Remember — to avoid heartache:
(and homicide for goodness' sake!)
your friend must share the blend with you,
not be blended in there too*.

Even for besties, cannibalism
has been known to cause a schism.

*unless they've had a good enough innings,
and you don't want to split the lottery winnings.

Dragon Fruit* Dreams

Do you suffer from nightmares?
Such a rotten state of affairs.

What you need for a restful night
is dragon fruit – a pure delight!

Seed-speckled morsels calm your sleep
sparking dreams of fluffy sheep.

Say goodnight to nightmare dramas
slumber tonight with fleecy llamas.

Don't let nightmares drive you crackers
fill your dreams with soft alpacas.

79

Broccoli Bravery

A GREAT CURE FOR NERVOUSNESS: BROCCOLI-HUGGING!
FEAR-NO-MORE SPIDERS, OUTSIDERS, OR MUGGING!
THE MUNCHING OF FLORETS, TENDER AND RARE,
WILL EVEN GIVE COURAGE TO HUG A GREAT BEAR!

Part 7
Martial Artistry

Satsuma Samurai

Samurai skills are dead easy to get...
forget years of practice, toil, tears and sweat!

A thrice-daily habit of scoffing satsuma
will soon enough put you in very good humour;

Some even say it improves your digestion;
but not many know it also, without question,

Helps with a host of desirable knacks,
such as handling a samurai sword, or an axe.

Nectarine Ninja

Ninjas are stealthy and never get caught –
though they tiptoe around in the dark quite a lot...

They never trip over a book on the floor
or upset a lamp or bump into a door.

Nectarine Ninja's the best of the bunch,
from eating a nectarine each day at lunch.

Sweet nectarines, juicy and dripping,
the best ninja fuel, and a guard against tripping.

Kiwi Kung Fu

To earn a black belt in the art of kung fu,
fruit of the kiwi you must chew.

Kung fu skills are subtle, balanced, and elegant
like a grass-green kiwi fruit (if that seems relevant).

Cut open a kiwi along its equator
consider the pips — then eat it up later.

Confucius explained: *everything has beauty,
but it is not something all people can see.*

Jalapeño Happiness

Jalapeños give
quite a kick...

Filled with cheese
and fried on a stick.

Is happiness a martial art?

Yes, coz it kicks total arse!